Ring-a-ring o' roses,
A pocket full of posies,
A-tishoo! A-tishoo!
We all fall down.

Other Books by Marguerite de Angeli

Marguerite de Angeli's

A POCKET FULL
OF POSIES

A MERRY MOTHER GOOSE

DOUBLEDAY & COMPANY, INC.

GARDEN CITY, NEW YORK

Selections from BOOK OF NURSERY AND MOTHER GOOSE RHYMES.
Copyright © 1954, 1961, by Marguerite de Angeli Library of Congress Card Number 61–11142
Lithographed in the U.S.A. All Rights Reserved
9 8 7 6 5 4 3

Pat-a-cake, pat-a-cake, baker's man,
Bake me a cake as fast as you can;
Pat it and prick it, and mark it with B,
Put it in the oven for baby and me.

Bye, baby bunting,
Daddy's gone a-hunting,
To get a little rabbit's skin,
To wrap a baby bunting in.

Dance to your Daddy,
My little babby;
Dance to your Daddy,
   My little lamb.

You shall have a fishy
In a little dishy;
You shall have a fishy
   When the boat comes in.

Dance, little baby, dance up high:
Never mind, baby, mother is by;
Crow and caper, caper and crow,
There, little baby, there you go;

6

Up to the ceiling, down to the ground,
Backwards and forwards, round and round:
Dance, little baby, and mother shall sing,
With the merry gay choral, ding, ding-a-ding, ding.

Here sits the Lord Mayor,
                    ]*forehead*
Here sit his men,
                    ]*eyes*
Here sits the cockadoodle,
                    ]*right cheek*
Here sits the hen,
                    ]*left cheek*
Here sit the little chickens,
                    ]*tip of the nose*
Here they run in,
                    ]*mouth*
Chin chopper, chin chopper, chin chopper, chin.
                    ]*chuck the chin*

Brow, brow, brinkie,
Eye, eye, winkie,
Mouth, mouth, merry,
Cheek, cheek, cherry,
Chin-chopper, chin-chopper.

Eye winker,
Tom Tinker,
Nose dropper,
Mouth eater,
Chin-chopper, chin-chopper.

                    ]*Baby's face*

There was an old woman who lived in a shoe,
She had so many children she didn't know what to do;
She gave them some broth without any bread;
She whipped them all soundly and put them to bed.

Hush-a-bye, baby, on the tree top,
When the wind blows the cradle will rock;
When the bough breaks the cradle will fall,
Down will come baby, cradle, and all.

Brow bender,
Eye peeper,
Nose dreeper,
Mouth eater,
Chin chopper,
Knock at the door,
Ring the bell,
Lift up the latch,
Walk in . . .
Take a chair
Sit by there,
How d'you do this morning?

] *Baby's face*

Great A, little a,
  Bouncing B,
The cat's in the cupboard
  And can't see me.

This little pig went to market,
This little pig stayed at home,
This little pig had roast beef,
This little pig had none,
And this little pig cried, Wee-wee-wee-wee-wee,
  I can't find my way home.

] *A rhyme for five toes*

To market, to market,
  To buy a plum bun:
Home again, home again,
  Market is done.

To market, to market, to buy a fat pig,
Home again, home again, jiggety-jig;

To market, to market, to buy a fat hog,
Home again, home again, jiggety-jog.

  Shoe a little horse,
  Shoe a little mare,
But let the little coltie go bare, bare, bare.

Ride a cock-horse to Banbury Cross,
To see a fine lady upon a white horse;
Rings on her fingers and bells on her toes,
And she shall have music wherever she goes.

8

See-saw, sacradown,
Which is the way to London town?
One foot up and the other foot down,
That is the way to London town.

There were two blackbirds
    Sat upon a hill,
The one was nam'd Jack,
    The other nam'd Jill;
Fly away Jack,
    Fly away Jill,
Come again Jack,
    Come again Jill.

How many miles to Babylon?
Three score miles and ten.
Can I get there by candle-light?

Yes, and back again.
If your heels are nimble and light,
You may get there by candle-light.

Pease porridge hot,
Pease porridge cold,
Pease porridge in the pot
Nine days old.

Some like it hot,
Some like it cold,
Some like it in the pot
Nine days old.

This is the way the ladies ride
Tri, tre, tre, tree!
Tri, tre, tre, tree!
This is the way the ladies ride
Tri, tre, tre, tri-tre-tre, tree!

]*A game for hands*

This is the way the gentlemen ride,
Gallop-a-trot, gallop-a-trot!
This is the way the gentlemen ride,
Gallop-a-gallop-a-trot!

Hot cross buns!
Hot cross buns!
One a penny, two a penny,
Hot cross buns!

This is the way the farmers ride,
Hobbledy-hoy, hobbledy-hoy!
This is the way the farmers ride,
Hobbledy-hobbledy-hoy!

If you have no daughters
Give them to your sons;
One a penny, two a penny,
Hot cross buns!

10

There was a little girl, and she had a little curl
   Right in the middle of her forehead;
When she was good, she was very, very good,
   But when she was bad, she was horrid.

   Cross-patch,
   Draw the latch,
Sit by the fire and spin;
   Take a cup,
   And drink it up,
Then call your neighbors in.

Little Betty Blue
Lost her holiday shoe,
What can little Betty do?
Give her another
To match the other,
And then she may walk out in two.

Little Miss Muffet
Sat on a tuffet,
Eating her curds and whey;
There came a big spider,
Who sat down beside her
And frightened Miss Muffet away.

Mary had a little lamb,
   Its fleece was white as snow;
And everywhere that Mary went
   The lamb was sure to go.

Little Jack Horner
Sat in the corner,
Eating a Christmas pie;
He put in his thumb,
And pulled out a plum,
And said, What a good boy am I!

It followed her to school one day,
   That was against the rule;
It made the children laugh and play
   To see a lamb at school.

And so the teacher turned it out,
   But still it lingered near;
And waited patiently about
   Till Mary did appear.

Mistress Mary, quite contrary,
   How does your garden grow?
With silver bells and cockle shells,
   And pretty maids all in a row.

"Why does the lamb love Mary so?"
   The eager children cry.
"Why, Mary loves the lamb, you know,"
   The teacher did reply.

Curly locks, Curly locks,
  Wilt thou be mine?
Thou shalt not wash dishes
  Nor yet feed the swine,
But sit on a cushion
  And sew a fine seam,
And feed upon strawberries,
  Sugar and cream.

Monday's child is fair of face,
Tuesday's child is full of grace,
Wednesday's child is full of woe,
Thursday's child has far to go,
Friday's child is loving and giving,
Saturday's child works hard for his living,
And the child that is born on the Sabbath day
Is bonny and blithe, and good and gay.

One, two,
Buckle my shoe;
Three, four,
Knock at the door;
Five, six,
Pick up sticks;
Seven, eight,
Lay them straight;
Nine, ten,
A big fat hen;

Eleven, twelve,
Dig and delve;
Thirteen, fourteen,
Maids a-courting;
Fifteen, sixteen,
Maids in the kitchen;
Seventeen, eighteen,
Maids in waiting;
Nineteen, twenty,
My plate's empty.

Little Bo-peep has lost her sheep,
  And can't tell where to find them;
Leave them alone, and they'll come home,
  And bring their tails behind them.

Little Bo-peep fell fast asleep,
  And dreamt she heard them bleating;
But when she awoke, she found it a joke,
  For they were still all fleeting.

Then up she took her little crook,
  Determined for to find them;
She found them indeed, but it made her heart bleed,
  For they'd left their tails behind them.

Cock-a-doodle-doo!
My dame has lost her shoe,
My master's lost his fiddlestick,
And knows not what to do.

Cock-a-doodle-doo!
What is my dame to do?
Till master finds his fiddlestick,
She'll dance without her shoe.

What are little boys made of, made of?
What are little boys made of?
"Snips and snails, and puppy-dogs' tails;
And that's what little boys are made of, made of."

What are little girls made of, made of?
What are little girls made of?
"Sugar and spice, and all that's nice;
And that's what little girls are made of, made of."

Georgie Porgie, pudding and pie,
Kissed the girls and made them cry;
When the boys came out to play,
Georgie Porgie ran away.

Rub-a-dub-dub,
Three men in a tub;
And who do you think they be?
The butcher, the baker,
The candlestick-maker;
They all jumped out of a rotten potato,
Turn 'em out, knaves all three!

Simple Simon met a pieman
  Going to the fair;
Says Simple Simon to the pieman,
  "Let me taste your ware."

Says the pieman to Simple Simon,
  "Show me first your penny;"
Says Simple Simon to the pieman,
  "Indeed, I have not any."

Simple Simon went to look
  If plums grew on a thistle;
He pricked his fingers very much,
  Which made poor Simon whistle.

He went to catch a dickey-bird,
  And thought he could not fail,
Because he'd got a little salt
  To put upon its tail.

Simple Simon went a-fishing
  For to catch a whale;
All the water he had got,
  Was in his mother's pail.

Humpty Dumpty sat on a wall,
Humpty Dumpty had a great fall.
    All the king's horses,
    And all the king's men,
Couldn't put Humpty together again.

Baa, baa, black sheep,
    Have you any wool?
Yes, sir, yes, sir,
    Three bags full;
One for the master,
    And one for the dame,
And one for the little boy
    Who lives down the lane.

Bow, wow, wow,
Whose dog art thou?
Little Tom Tinker's dog,
Bow, wow, wow.

Barber, barber, shave a pig,
How many hairs will make a wig?
"Four and twenty, that's enough."
Give the poor barber a pinch of snuff.

Lucy Locket lost her pocket,
Kitty Fisher found it;
Not a penny was there in it,
Only ribbon round it.

Pussy cat, pussy cat, where have you been?
I've been to London to look at the queen.
Pussy cat, pussy cat, what did you there?
I frightened a little mouse under her chair.

A diller, a dollar,
A ten o'clock scholar,
What makes you come so soon?
You used to come at ten o'clock,
But now you come at noon.

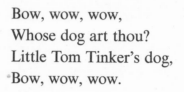

Dickery, dickery, dare,
The pig flew up in the air;
The man in brown soon brought him down,
Dickery, dickery, dare.

Little Tommy Tittlemouse
Lived in a little house;
He caught fishes
In other men's ditches.

Ladybird, ladybird
   Fly away home,
Your house is on fire
   And your children all gone;
All except one
   And that's little Ann
And she has crept under
   The warming pan.

Ding dong bell
Pussy's in the well.
Who put her in?
Little Tommy Green.
Who pulled her out?
Little Johnny Stout.
What a naughty boy was that
To try to drown poor pussy cat,
Who never did him any harm,
But killed the mice in his father's barn.

Hey diddle diddle,
The cat and the fiddle,
The cow jumped over the moon.

The little dog laughed
To see such sport,
And the dish ran away with the spoon.

See-saw, Margery Daw,
Jacky shall have a new master;
Jacky must have but a penny a day,
Because he can't work any faster.

Hickory, dickory, dock,
The mouse ran up the clock.
The clock struck one,
The mouse ran down,
Hickory, dickory, dock.

Hickety, pickety, my black hen,
She lays eggs for gentlemen;
Gentlemen come every day
To see what my black hen doth lay.
Sometimes nine and sometimes ten,
Hickety, pickety, my black hen.

Hark, hark,
The dogs do bark,
The beggars are coming to town;
Some in rags,
And some in tags,
And one in a velvet gown.

If wishes were horses,
    Then beggars would ride;
If turnips were watches,
    I'd wear one by my side.

Solomon Grundy,
Born on a Monday,
Christened on Tuesday,
Married on Wednesday,
Took ill on Thursday,
Worse on Friday,
Died on Saturday,
Buried on Sunday.
This is the end
Of Solomon Grundy.

There was a crooked man, and he walked a crooked mile,
He found a crooked sixpence against a crooked stile;
He bought a crooked cat, which caught a crooked mouse,
And they all lived together in a little crooked house.

Yankee Doodle came to town,
    Riding on a pony;
He stuck a feather in his cap
    And called it macaroni.

Old King Cole
Was a merry old soul,
And a merry old soul was he;
He called for his pipe,
And he called for his bowl,
And he called for his fiddlers three.

Every fiddler, he had a fiddle,
And a very fine fiddle had he;
Twee tweedle dee, tweedle dee, went the fiddlers.
Oh, there's none so rare
As can compare
With King Cole and his fiddlers three.

Sing a song of sixpence
    A pocket full of rye;
Four and twenty blackbirds
    Baked in a pie.

When the pie was opened,
    The birds began to sing;
Was not that a dainty dish
    To set before the king?

The king was in his counting-house
    Counting out his money;
The queen was in the parlor
    Eating bread and honey.

The maid was in the garden
    Hanging out the clothes,
Along came a blackbird
    And nipped off her nose.

Gay go up and gay go down,
To ring the bells of London Town.

Bull's eyes and targets,
Say the bells of St. Margaret's.

Brickbats and tiles,
Say the bells of St. Giles'.

Halfpence and farthings,
Say the bells of St. Martin's.

Oranges and lemons,
Say the bells of St. Clement's.

Pancakes and fritters,
Say the bells of St. Peter's.

Two sticks and an apple,
Say the bells at Whitechapel.

Old Father Baldpate,
Say the slow bells at Aldgate.

Pokers and tongs,
Say the bells of St. John's.

Kettles and pans,
Say the bells of St. Anne's.

You owe me ten shillings,
Say the bells of St. Helen's.

When will you pay me?
Say the bells at Old Bailey.

When I grow rich,
Say the bells at Shoreditch.

Pray when will that be?
Say the bells of Stepney.

I am sure I don't know,
Says the great bell at Bow.

Here comes a candle to light you to bed,
And here comes a chopper to chop off your head.

The rose is red, the violet blue,
The gillyflower sweet, and so are you.
These are the words you bade me say
For a pair of new gloves on Easter day.

Jack Sprat could eat no fat,
    His wife could eat no lean,
And so betwixt them both, you see,
    They licked the platter clean.

Rain, rain, go away,
Come again another day.

Here we go round the mulberry bush,
The mulberry bush, the mulberry bush,
Here we go round the mulberry bush.
On a cold and frosty morning.

This is the way we wash our hands,
Wash our hands, wash our hands,
This is the way we wash our hands,
On a cold and frosty morning.

This is the way we wash our clothes,
Wash our clothes, wash our clothes,
This is the way we wash our clothes,
On a cold and frosty morning.

This is the way we go to school,
Go to school, go to school,
This is the way we go to school,
On a cold and frosty morning.

This is the way we come out of school,
Come out of school, come out of school,
This is the way we come out of school,
On a cold and frosty morning.

March winds and April showers
Bring forth May flowers.

Jack and Jill went up the hill
    To fetch a pail of water;
Jack fell down and broke his crown,
    And Jill came tumbling after.

Up got Jack, and home did trot,
    As fast as he could caper,
To old Dame Dob, who patched his nob
    With vinegar and brown paper.

Here's Sulky Sue,
What shall we do?
Turn her face to the wall
Till she comes to.

Blow, wind, blow! and go, mill, go!
That the miller may grind his corn;
    That the baker may take it,
    And into rolls make it,
And bring us some hot in the morn.

Little Robin Redbreast
   Sat upon a rail;
Niddle noddle went his head,
   Wiggle waggle went his tail.

Little Boy Blue,
   Come blow your horn,
The sheep's in the meadow,
   The cow's in the corn;
But where is the boy
   Who looks after the sheep?
He's under a haycock,
   Fast asleep.
Will you wake him?
   No, not I,
For if I do,
   He's sure to cry.

Goosey, goosey, gander,
   Whither shall I wander?
Upstairs and downstairs
   And in my lady's chamber.

There I met an old man
   Who would not say his prayers.
I took him by the left leg
   And threw him down the stairs.

Wee Willie Winkie runs through the town,
Upstairs and downstairs in his nightgown,
Rapping at the window, crying through the lock,
"Are the children in their beds, for now it's eight o'clock?"

Deedle, deedle, dumpling, my son John,
Went to bed with his trousers on;
One shoe off, and one shoe on,
Deedle, deedle, dumpling, my son John.

Matthew, Mark, Luke and John,
Bless the bed that I lie on.
   Four corners to my bed,
   Four angels round my head;
   One to watch and one to pray
   And two to bear my soul away.

God bless the master of this house,
Likewise the mistress too,
And all the little children
That round the table go;

And all your kin and kinsmen,
That dwell both far and near;
I wish you a Merry Christmas,
And a Happy New Year.

INDEX

30